# Reaching Your Potential

## 5 STEPS FROM SURVIVING TO THRIVING

JOAN WIPPERFURTH

Reaching Your Potential: 5 Steps from Surviving to Thriving

To contact the author, visit
coach.wellcoach.com/joan-wipperfurth
or
joanfitandfreehealthconsulting@yahoo.com

ISBN: 978-0-692-53416-8

Printed in the United States of America

# TABLE OF CONTENTS

## *DEDICATION*

I dedicate this book to my husband, Herman, who has fully supported me in going after my dreams and all of the things that matter to me over the last four years of our marriage. And to my best friend Megan, who has been there for me over the last ten years. She came into my life when I was just beginning to take my journey forward. Her honesty, love, listening ear and support have enriched my life.

I will never forget all of the love and support I received during the worst of times, especially from Diane, Denise and Deb. Each of you held me up in unique ways when I couldn't walk alone. Even though we don't see each other very often, you all have a very special place in my heart.

# PART 1
# THE PAST

# In Darkness and Despair

## CHAPTER ONE

*"I HAVE LEARNED THAT PEOPLE WILL FORGET WHAT YOU SAID, PEOPLE WILL FORGET WHAT YOU DID, BUT PEOPLE WILL NEVER FORGET HOW YOU MADE THEM FEEL."*

*-MAYA ANGELOU*

I grew up in a suburb of Minneapolis, raised by both parents, in a home where I always knew I was loved. I have a lot of great memories in the early years of my childhood. We had a cabin on Star Island at Cass Lake where summers were filled with so many fun adventures. We did not have electricity or running water so there was no TV or video games. Each summer, we would read long books like The Poseidon Adventure or Gone with the Wind and then swap with a friend for another one. We played cards and games and had so much old fashioned fun. We hiked the island and watched the bald eagles fly overhead. Each of us kids learned to water ski and spent hours each day in the water swimming, floating on rafts, and boating. It was a big deal when we got old enough to take the boat out on our own. We would pack up a lunch and head out on an adventure, cruising around the island and come back laughing and sunburned.

My dad would take us out fishing in the evenings and we would fill the boat with little sunfish that my dad spent hours filleting so that my mom could make us a fish fry. My mom loved to make massive pancakes for breakfast and my brothers would have pancake eating contests. It was such a happy time.

In the spring of 1974, when I was fourteen, my parents sold the cabin so we could have some different family adventures. We planned to do some travelling around the country starting the next summer.

That fall, my twenty-two year old brother went up to the lake with a bunch of guys to duck hunt. We had sold our big boat to the new cabin owners and the young guys had to cross a five mile section of water in the twelve foot fishing boat we still owned. Two trips with guys and supplies made it to the island safely. The last boat, filled with four young men, did not make it to the island campsite. On October 5, 1974, which is also my father's birthday, we found out that my brother, my cousin, another cousin's fiancée, and one other young man had capsized. All were assumed dead from hypothermia. Our family's lives changed overnight.

My dad was devastated and went up to the lake right away to help with the search for the bodies. My mom was in Boston with my twin brother for the weekend. They waited until she came home two days later to tell her. My brother, Gary, was the first one to be found the day after my mom got back. Then, the next day, my cousin Glen was found. And a few days after that, my cousin's fiancée, David, was found. They were close to the point of having to give up the search for the year due to the frigid water and the diver's safety when the last young man was found. This was also the day that my brother and cousin were buried. October 14th also happened to be my parent's twenty-fourth wedding anniversary.

My dad blamed himself and suffered miserably. He thought that if he had been there that they would have been safe. My dad was not to blame. These were grown, young men that didn't need or want parental chaperoning. But he was beside himself. He turned to alcohol to drown his sorrows. He spent most days on the basement couch, having masked his anguish with alcohol.

My heart was broken. Gary was my big brother. I looked up to him so much. One fond memory I have with Gary came as a result of hearing noises in a neighbor's home while babysitting one night when I was thirteen. I was afraid and thought someone was in the house. I noticed the kitchen light had just come on at my house next door. Gary had just come home. I called him and told him I thought someone was in the neighbor's house and to please come over. He came right over with a bat in his hand and, in his typical lighthearted way, made me go first as we wandered the house, finding nothing out of the norm. I looked up to him, and now he was gone.

My mom's heart was shattered and she was consumed with grief. Just three days earlier, I had watched my mom say goodbye to Gary. She had just finished washing her hair and had her head wrapped up in a towel. She gave him a big hug and a kiss and told him she loved him. He lived in his own apartment and my mom always loved it when he'd stop by, usually at mealtime, knowing my mom would love to feed him. It was so hard to see her hurting so bad.

My mom did her best to keep it together but she was also dealing with so much of her own pain. I hated that life had changed so much and that my parents were so different. There was no more laughter in our home. We all just went through the motions of daily living. I got into the wrong crowd for a short time and experimented with drugs, causing my mom extra grief for about a year. My older brother was also struggling and got into a lot more trouble, which lasted for about three years. She really had her hands full trying to hold things together with minimal help from my dad.

Sometimes my dad would get drunk and say horrible things to us when he was mad. He used to call me his "cutie pie" or "sweetie pie," and now he would tell me to get out if I didn't like things the way they were. I wanted to leave but I was only sixteen. I missed my dad.

My dad had experienced a tough childhood. He wasn't taught good values or given any spiritual training. He had no healthy coping skills and no personal faith to cling to. My mom had a totally opposite upbringing. She had grown up in an overly zealous, "revival tent meeting" type of setting. She thought her parents were too strict, but was also very grateful for her faith, which has always been her foundation. She went through a normal grieving process and came out stronger in the end. I am convinced it is due to her faith, which she worked hard to instill in her kids.

Their marriage struggled for years. My dad got into a few affairs. I saw him in bed with another woman once. My mom left him shortly after that and took my twin brother and me with her. We moved into a tiny, old mobile home in the same town of our nice family home. One night, my dad showed up and started yelling outside the door, telling her he'd keep her in court until all the money was gone if she didn't come back home. We did a short time later. At the time, she felt she had no other choice. Her income was too small to take care of us kids and my dad was totally irrational at the time and probably would have followed through on his threat. My dad eventually went to Alcoholics Anonymous and got help. He found work and my mom and dad managed to work through their marriage problems.

I did not understand then how deeply traumatic events change a person. Life crises can either destroy us or force us to grow and become stronger. All I knew at the time was that my family had been devastated and everything was different. Gone was the laughter and lightheartedness in our home. My dad still loved us but he didn't seem able to recover from the loss of his son. I missed my normal home life and moved out just a few months after graduating from high school.

Even though our home was filled with anger and sadness during my high school years, there were also some good times. It was just very different. It was my mom who instigated anything fun. I know she had to really force herself to move on for us, while still really struggling on her own. My mom had always loved travel and decided we should still have some good memories after Gary's death. She desperately needed it too. Day-to-day home life was tough, but she was committed to doing what she could to keep life somewhat normal.

I recall a few times she packed us three kids up with a small tent, a cooler and the Coleman cook stove for a cross-country driving adventure. One trip had us exploring all of eastern Canada. We went all the way out to Nova Scotia and got to attend the Scottish Highland festival. I'd never heard how beautiful the bagpipes could be. One morning, while in the camp rest room, I found my mom crying at the sink as she attempted to wash her face. I asked her what was wrong. She said the water was freezing and it reminded her of the pain her son must have experienced as his young body froze to death. What a horrible thing for a mother to ponder.

Another time we went west and experienced the Rocky mountains, the Calgary Stampede, and went all the way out to Vancouver Island where we ocean fished. I caught a thirty-five pound cod and we only had one cooler. My mom went around asking fellow campers if they wanted fresh fish for their dinner. She had spunk and instilled in us the love for travel and adventure.

The other positive part of my high school years was when I got involved with the high school youth group at church as well as with school activities. I also met Doug when I was fifteen. We dated all through high school, attending all the dances, and then he asked me to marry him the summer after I graduated high school. He was just one year older than me. He came from a good family and I was head over heels in love with him. My parents loved him and were totally supportive of us marrying so young. We married a year later on a snowy night in March during his spring break at the University of Minnesota. We had a ten day dream honeymoon in Jamaica and then began our young lives together.

Doug went to the University of Minnesota and worked part time as a courier driver. I went to school for travel agency management. We were broke but in love and learned the value of working hard and working towards a better future together. I worked as a travel agent for a few years and then found my dream job as the manager of Brighton Travel. I loved my job and Doug and I got to do a lot of fun, inexpensive travelling around the country. I went to Alaska and toured Europe during that time.

Soon after, our young family started. First, it was a chubby, adorable little golden retriever puppy named King, and then about six months later, came our first child. He was a little, six pound baby boy. We named him Gary, in honor of my brother. He brought so much joy into our lives and also seemed to bring further healing for my parents. They were thrilled that we named him Gary and they loved spending time with him. I realized that becoming a parent was changing me. It was harder than I expected it to be, but it was also the most satisfying thing I'd ever done. I found myself forgiving my father for the pain he had caused me. I knew that I would do the best I could as a mother, and I realized that he had done the same. I was now an example for other lives, and I wanted to be a role model for forgiveness as well. I quit my full-time job within nine months of Gary's birth. I loved being a mom.

A few years later, our little blue-eyed "Shell Bell" (Michelle) came bounding into our world on the coldest night of 1989. Her eyes were so big and beautiful that we nicknamed her "Plates." She won a baby photo contest at six months old. Our small townhouse was bursting at the seams. At this point, we started looking for country property not too far from Minneapolis. We were able to find sixteen high, wooded acres just east of Cambridge. It was a spectacular property with hundred year old oaks, pine trees and maples. Doug and toddler Gary went to work clearing the land. Gary would ride on his dad's lap while he cleared brush with the tractor we rented. I would come up with picnic food and enjoy just being there with Michelle in the playpen. Sometimes, we would have a small fire and wiener roast. About a year later, we moved into our dream home in the country.

A few years later, our third blessing was born. Little Matthew came out smiling and brought so much joy into our lives. Michelle adored him, and he followed her around like a little puppy. He was the happiest, most easy going little guy you'd ever seen. He was nicknamed "Mafoo Man." We felt extremely blessed to have three healthy children and a beautiful home and environment to raise them in.

We created a happy life in Cambridge. We had a good church, home, and families we were close with. I homeschooled the kids for several years. During that time, we had a huge country garden and a dozen fruit trees. I canned, froze and dehydrated fresh produce. Our basement pantry was filled with canning jars of all the fun things we'd produced from our own land. I made fresh homemade bread every week. The kids were involved with 4-H, which stands for Future Farmers of America. They participated in the county fair each July and showed animals and garden produce. The kids all had chores and learned to work for the things they wanted. Doug travelled a lot over the years and I felt like a single mom quite often. But we were a team, each doing our part to take care of our wonderful family. When Doug was home, he was all about his family, and he did his best to schedule travel around the kid's sporting events when possible. As a result of his heavy travel schedule, we were able to take a lot of fun, relatively inexpensive trips over the years, utilizing the frequent flyer miles and hotel bonuses he earned. We also had a pop-up tent trailer and loved spending time at the state parks on the north shore of Lake Superior. There, we'd hike, fish and enjoy a big fire every evening where the kids would enjoy S'mores. When Matt was little, he used to say that the best part of camping was roasting marshmallows.

Doug was a committed, loving father and husband. We went out on a date every Saturday night and took at least one weekend away as a couple each year. We made our marriage a priority and, as a result, enjoyed a happy marriage for twenty-four years. My mother said she could see how much he adored me by the way he looked at me and held me. Many summer evenings, we would take the kids on a walk after dinner. Doug and I would kiss in front of them once in a while and, of course, the kids would think that was gross. Doug would tell them, "At least you know your mom and dad love each other." It was a good life.

While Doug was working his way up in the courier industry, I was at home with the kids. I earned my degree in holistic nutrition and was very involved on the school board for our local private school. I also helped start a local homeschool group for about sixty kids in the area. I was involved in leadership in various roles in our local church including children's, women's and library ministries. My life revolved around my family and community, and I was very much fulfilled.

Doug advanced in his industry and was respected and sought after by local and national courier services over the years. He knew the business inside and out and was good at it. In 2000, I helped him establish his own delivery business. It was a huge challenge, both financially and timewise, but it was his dream and I believed he would be successful so I did everything I could to help him. We were living on one income and had to be extra frugal to get this business up and running successfully. Putting everything on the line, his dream was born. We supported each other's dreams and after a few tough years, things started to stabilize and the business became a success. I had originally planned to help him for a few months, but that few months turned into a few years of working at our company, and then going home each afternoon to homeschool the kids. We were both exhausted. We were now in the place where we were able to hire another employee to take my place so I could get back to the family. Our country homestead, along with three growing children and their activities took a lot of time.

The next few years were good. The business was stabilizing and Doug was home more. Finances eased up and it seemed like everything was falling into place. We bought a timeshare and started taking really nice family vacations to different Mexican resorts. In March of 2004, we took a family trip to Puerto Vallarta. We were there for our 24th wedding anniversary. My parents came along too. The kids had fun playing mini-golf, ping pong, and spending lots of time in the pool. My parents would watch the kids so Doug and I could go out for a few evenings alone. One night, we went to a romantic little restaurant on the beach. We felt so blessed and started planning what we wanted to do for our 25th anniversary the following year. We decided we would go to the Riviera Maya, just south of Cancun, and spend ten nights at the Moon Palace. He told me that he wanted to buy me a bigger diamond for our anniversary. When we got home from that trip, we started jewelry shopping and found a beautiful stone and a new setting. He planned to have me wait until the following March to get it, but he was so excited for me to have it that I got it ten months early. He told me that he wanted others to see how much he loved me. Everything about his behavior showed him to be a man still very much in love and committed to his wife.

Things started to change in the fall of that year. Our oldest child went off to college and we had two teenagers left at home. I had some concerns with things that Doug started saying about the woman I helped hire. Doug always had great boundaries with women in the workplace. I never worried about him, even when he travelled. The things he was saying about her were not the kinds of things he would normally notice about other women. I told him that his conversations sounded inappropriate to be having with an employee. He would just change the subject and I would feel uneasy. This went on for a few months before my uneasiness increased.

In January of 2005, Doug picked me up at the airport after I returned from a girl's trip to Mexico. Something was very different about him. He would not look me in the eye. We always looked each other in the eyes when we talked. I knew then that something had happened between them. He repeatedly said that nothing was going on. I desperately wanted to believe him. It was so out of character for Doug to be acting this way.

A few months later, we went to Mexico for our 25th wedding anniversary. Everything was planned for a wonderful, romantic celebration. I was counting on this trip being a time that we would sort out what was going on and just have some fun together. I could not have been more disappointed. Here we were, at a beautiful resort on the ocean, spending a small fortune to celebrate twenty-five years of marriage. But he was distant and on his phone a lot, saying that he needed to check in with the office. I felt like I was the only one who cared about our relationship. Our conversations were strained and he would not look me in the eyes. He was easily angered and he decided to leave before our ten days was up. He said that he needed a few days alone to work through some things he was dealing with. He repeatedly said that I hadn't done anything and that he just had some inner struggles he was trying to deal with. It didn't make any sense to me. We had prepaid the trip so I stayed the last three nights alone. I was so afraid for our marriage and for our family.

My emotions were all over the place. The kids had no idea what was going on. They thought I was being crabby. I hadn't told a soul yet what I suspected was going on. I kept wondering if I was imagining the affair. I hoped I was imagining it and that something else was going on that he hadn't yet shared. I had three children's lives to consider and I still had no proof, so I kept it all to myself. My heart was heavily burdened and I had never felt so alone in life before. Every night, I crawled into bed with a man who had become a stranger to me.

It was several long, very emotional months later that I caught him at her townhouse. I was devastated and in shock. This man was the love of my life. I felt like I was watching someone else's life when I saw him walk out of her front door. It was like watching a priceless vase fall from a shelf and shatter into a million pieces. Only it was my heart that was shattered. I couldn't believe my eyes. Doug gave me the strangest look when he saw me. It was like he wanted to be caught. I didn't recognize this new person he had become. I asked him to leave the house that day.

That evening, Gary came home from Bethel to be with Michelle and Matt while Doug told the children what he had done and why he had to leave. Only Gary had suspected what was going on. The pain of watching my children being told that their life was being torn apart was the worst moment in my life. It was unbearable for everyone. It was so unbelievably unfair. They hadn't done anything, yet everything about their lives was changing and they had no say in any of it. And I couldn't protect them or fix it.

I offered Doug forgiveness and a second chance if he would go to counseling and fire her. He said he would like to "eventually" save the marriage, but was unwilling to get rid of her. He said it was unfair for her to lose her job. Instead, he chose to lose his wife and family.

The depression I felt was overwhelming. I am normally a very positive, upbeat person, but I was crying all of the time and pulled away from most of my friends. I hardly slept for the next nine months and I lost twenty pounds. I quit smiling. I felt so alone in my pain. I was in total denial that my marriage was over. I never thought this could happen between us. We always said that we would be the cute, little old couple walking the beach hand in hand.

I counseled with my pastor. He tried to talk with Doug as well. I also went to a professional counselor to help me through my grieving process. She was very helpful and I saw her for about a year. She suggested that I start a gratitude journal and write out three things each day I was grateful for. I did, and some days I really had to stretch to feel thankful, but it helped me focus on what was still good. I still had my children with me. I was very grateful for that. She also encouraged me to do something nice for myself each day. It might be just taking a bubble bath, listening to calming music, or reading a fun book. I changed a few things around the house because everything reminded me of what we had built together and it hurt to be there. Yet, I wanted to be in my home with my children, but now it felt like a mausoleum of memories. Making some changes helped me to remain in the home. Doug and I both agreed we wanted that for the kids.

I learned the importance of having a good support system during that time. My support system consisted of a counselor, a pastor, and several close girl-friends. Some friends would just call and check in on me regularly. They always seemed to have time to talk when I needed a friend to listen. Some prayed with me. Having people show they cared for me by listening was powerful. Very few people seem to be good listeners. I learned to really value and cherish those that had developed the loving skill of active listening. One night, my girlfriend, Diane, drove four hours just to be with me. She said that I cried all night with an eeriness that she'd never heard before. She, along with her husband, Quintin, were key supporters for me during that awful time in my life. I will never forget how much they loved and supported me.

I loved being married and having a family. I loved having a close companion to share my life with daily. I loved having someone that knew me better than anyone else call during the day just to hear how my day was going. We would talk about the kids, our business, and all the other parts of daily living. We had been a great team. Then he was simply gone. I had been home with my kids for almost twenty years. Here I was, at forty-three, having to think about finding a career that would support me for the second half of my life. I had always been such a strong person but I didn't feel strong at all now. At the time, my personal identity was mostly tied to my marriage. Yet, there was no marriage left. Even my pastor was telling me it was okay to file for divorce. But I wasn't ready yet.

Several months later, I went to Mexico with my daughter for a week and then stayed for another week alone. She and I had a lot of fun and it was a sort of reprieve from daily life for both of us. I knew that home wasn't what it used to be and I so desperately wanted to give her some time away from it all. Doug was spending more time with Matt and taking him on hunting and fishing trips.

My second week alone was filled with so many different emotions. I had never spent a week on vacation alone before. I felt lonely a lot of the time. It was especially hard to see couples together and families laughing and making memories like we used to. It was hard to go to a restaurant alone, surrounded by tables full of happy looking vacationers. We had been at this same resort a few years prior with the whole family and it had been a great vacation. I recalled the boys out flying through the waves on jet skis and all the kids parasailing overhead. That was never going to happen again. It was painful. I couldn't imagine ever being happy again.

My counselor encouraged me to use this second week of the trip for rest. I had struggled with some physical issues as a result of all the stress. My body just needed to calm down mentally and physically. I knew that I would have to file for divorce soon but my body needed to be stronger to handle that next step. I walked the beach twice a day, napped poolside, and spent a lot of time reading both fiction and inspirational books. I have always been nurtured by good books. And I wrote in my journal.

I knew I couldn't keep living in limbo, yet I still did not want to be a divorced woman. I still wanted my happy family back. Everything in me cried out how wrong this situation was. Yet I knew that I had to accept my reality, no matter how much my heart rebelled against it. The marriage had been over for well over a year at this point and there were no signs of anything changing.

The morning I left, I decided to take one last walk on the beach. I have always loved the ocean more than any place. I stood in awe as the waves rolled in and out. Listening to the sound of them crashing in mesmerized me. I could have stood there all day. I have always sensed God's presence in nature, but this particular morning was very different. It was a sacred moment for me. I felt like God literally spoke into my heart the words, "It is finished." I remember tears rolling down my face, yet I had this amazing peace that washed over me as I continued to watch the waves roll in and out. It was a pivotal moment in my life. I knew then that I had the strength to go home and file for the divorce that needed to happen, and I did so one week later.

I struggled with the guilt of a failed marriage during this time. I thought that I must have done something to have this happen to our marriage. Doug told me repeatedly that it was his own issue and that I deserved better. It took me a long time to believe he was telling me the truth.

I experienced guilt as a single parent. I felt the kids needed us together to be good parents. Dealing with my own pain hampered my ability to be what they really needed. I had seen other single parents function better than I seemed to be doing. I was doing the best I could at the time, but by my own standards, I was not measuring up. That caused more guilt. Nothing felt right in my life.

My faith had always been so strong, but in my heartache, I questioned if God really cared. Intellectually, I knew that He did, but pain made me question how He could allow this to happen to me. So many had prayed for our marriage and family, yet it still dissolved. I thought, if He really controls the universe, how could He allow a solid family to break apart? I didn't understand why this was happening to me. Deep down, I knew that God was the only thing I could truly count on, but I couldn't feel it at the time and my emotions were ruling me. I knew that God gave each of us free will and that Doug had made his choice. I am grateful that God gives us free will and that we get to choose how we want to respond to his guidelines. I just wished that Doug had chosen differently. God didn't do anything wrong. I had to choose to read inspirational and hope-filled things to help pull me out of my slump. I found Joshua 1:9 to be comforting.

"Have I not commanded you? Be strong and courageous. Do not be afraid, and do not be dismayed, for the Lord your God is with you wherever you go."

I was not alone and that motivated me. I just had to get through one day, and then another, and then another. I had a growing sense of hope as the days went by, which I know was God's doing. I was given just enough strength to do what I had to do each day, nothing more, and nothing less.

I found a part-time job at a gym to be a wonderful distraction. There, I taught some group fitness classes, did some personal training, and ran some weight loss challenges. I only worked about twenty hours a week at the time but it was very helpful for me. Some days I would show up and think to myself, "How can I get through work today?" But as soon as I'd get involved in helping someone else, I'd find myself feeling better for a while. Being in a positive environment, getting good physical exercise, and working with a supportive manager made that job a very healthy thing for me. Knowing that I was positively affecting other people's lives was also helpful. Rich, the manager, became like a brother to me, and we worked to make the gym into a place where everyone was greeted and felt like they fit in. As I moved forward in my healing, I seemed to encounter other hurting people there. I felt better as I was able to encourage others that this season in life would also pass for them. I met so many wonderful people there and learned that there is some heartache in almost everyone you encounter. It taught me to be gentler with people and not to judge them so quickly. As I was vulnerable with others, I found many people opening up to me and sharing their heartache. I was just enough ahead of them to offer some hope.

As I look back, I realize that I was experiencing grief similar to that of a death. For me, it was harder than the deaths I'd experienced, including my brother and father. When someone dies, people all want to help. In divorce, you may be hurting as if a death occurred, yet others may judge you or think that you didn't try hard enough to save your marriage. I was dealing with the death of a relationship, an intact family, and all of our future plans and dreams.

As time went on, and some healing began, I finally realized that asking why was not going to help anything. I had to focus on the direction I would take to rebuild my life. It was very scary for me. I had to accept that I couldn't change someone else and that I had to take responsibility for what came next. I needed to do this for both my mental and my physical health. Too much stress over the past few years had taken its toll on me. I was exhausted and lacked my normal energy. I wasn't as patient as I wanted to be with my kids. I wasn't myself and I had a choice to make. Did I want to stay stuck, or did I want to accept the hand I'd been given and do what I had to do to move forward? It was about a two year process before I really found the strength that it would take to rebuild my life without Doug.

## Personal Application

Can you identify with parts of my story? Do you need to make some changes in your own life? If so, I encourage you to work through the questions here before moving on to Part 2.

1. Are you currently feeling stuck or stagnant in your life due to your own personal life crisis? What do you need to let go of, and what do you need to do to embrace a better future?

2. Consider what you really need to go forward in a healthy way. Do you need the assistance of a licensed counselor to help heal your past? Or maybe a health coach is more suitable to take you forward positively. What will help you to be your best self?

3. Where do you go for support? Do you have enough people in your life that will really listen to you, or do you need to build your support system?

Joan Wipperfurth

## PART 2
# THE JOURNEY FORWARD

# Heartache Teaches

## CHAPTER TWO - STEP 1

*"NOTHING GOES AWAY UNTIL IT TEACHES US WHAT WE NEED TO KNOW."*

*-PEMA CHODRON*

Have you noticed that you seem to grow the most from the things that are the hardest in your life? I was still hurting but I had to deal with my future. My survival instincts were starting to kick in. I had to think about what I would do for a career after so many years of being home with my kids. I had been a travel agency manager before the babies started coming and had taught some aerobic classes along the way. This was different. I was now in my early forties and I had to think about a career that would not only support myself but also allow for some retirement planning. And I had to navigate how to do all of that with two children still at home.

It was a very challenging time as all of our lives were completely disrupted. I remember praying, "God teach me everything I can learn from this so that this pain is not wasted." I believed that God was capable of using this heartache in a way that would make me better in some way. I had seen so many people over the years linger in anger and bitterness after a divorce. I didn't want to become an angry or bitter person that couldn't forgive people. I had to be intentional in forgiving over and over as things surfaced. I have always been a person that tries to see the good in others. I also knew that not forgiving another person was ultimately toxic for me. I couldn't keep reliving the offense if I wanted to be happy again. I had to work at letting go of past offenses as the negative feelings cropped up.

Learning to face fear head on was an important life lesson for me. During this confusing time, I thought back to something I had heard on the radio. There had been a woman speaking about how to tackle fear who suggested that whenever fear overpowers you, ask yourself this question, "What's the worst thing that could happen? And then what? And then what?" For instance, "What if I can't find a good job?" Then I'll have to start with a lesser job. "And then what?" Maybe I'll have to live some place less expensive. "And then what?" I could surely find some place to work and live. This concept helped me a lot when fear set in. It helped me to find perspective and direction. I had been in volunteer leadership positions over the years and had helped to establish a thriving business. I just needed to find new opportunities that would pay me.

Eleanor Roosevelt once said, "We gain strength, and courage, and confidence by each experience in which we really stop to look fear in the face. We must do that which we think we cannot." Facing some of the "what ifs" in life ahead of time can help to reduce anxious thoughts. I meditated on Philippians 4:6-7 which states, "Do not be anxious about anything, but in every situation, by prayer and petition, with thanksgiving, present your requests to God. And the peace of God, which transcends all understanding, will guard your hearts and your minds in Christ Jesus." Fear lessened its grip on me as I applied these strategies.

Uncertainty was another teacher to me. I spent the first twenty-four years in marriage feeling safe and secure and knew there were things I could count on. Sure, we had some hard things, but I knew we'd face them together. Then, all of a sudden, that safe harbor of marriage was gone. I had no clue what my future would look like. Things like where I'd live, if I'd be alone for the rest of my life, or if the kids would be okay all seemed so uncertain. I couldn't control much of what I was facing. Over time, I learned to get more comfortable with the uncertainties in life and focus on what I did have control over. I chose to focus on the opportunities ahead of me and look forward positively. Granted, this was a gradual process that I did well with some days, and not so good with on other days. I learned that I had to do everything I could to improve my situation while letting go of the things I couldn't control.

There were many things I needed to try to let go of. One of them was perfectionism. I could no longer be "super mom" while trying to figure out how to support myself after being home for so many years. I couldn't take care of everything around our large country property the same way I did when I had another person helping. I couldn't get to every sporting event with my job either, but I got to some of them. I had to make peace with that.

I had to let go of the feeling of being powerless. I may have been lacking my normal confidence and had my life turned upside down, but I was not powerless. I had always been a strong woman and just needed to find my way back to that by slowly taking charge of the skills that had served me in the past to deal with all of these new challenges.

I had to let go of fear. I worried about my financial future as a newly single woman with a lot of years ahead of me to live, and not much recent work experience. Corporate America had changed while I'd been home with my family. I had to just keep plugging along in spite of my fears.

I had to let go of not feeling safe and secure like I did while married to Doug. He had taken care of so many things and now so much was on me. I had to remind myself that God was ultimately in charge and that He was my only real security. That He promised to take care of me and to never leave me.

I had to let go of comparison. I was no longer a married woman like my friends. My life looked different than most of theirs. Holidays were hard and we had to try to find ways to celebrate when we were really wishing we had our family together.

I had to let go of feeling judged and not measuring up. I struggled to figure out how to be a single mom. It was hard trying to do things alone that I was used to doing as a couple. I had to remind myself that this was new for me and that I was doing the best I knew how at the time.

I had to really work at letting go of anxious thoughts. I worried about everything and had to use different tactics that helped to calm me. This took some time for me. I would pray. I would journal and meditate on inspirational thoughts that would feed my soul. I would listen to positive music in the car that would lift my spirits. I would take the time for a bubble bath and light some candles.

I had to let go of self-doubt. I wasn't doing as well as I thought I should be. I didn't make as much money as I needed to. I didn't have enough education or work experience for the better paying jobs. I really had to remind myself of what I was capable of and that I would get that experience as I worked.

I had to let go of control. I had to get comfortable with so many unfamiliar, new things. Most of what I was used to and comfortable with had changed. I had to tell myself that it would be okay and to just keep taking one step forward.

Lastly, I had to let go of the fear of failing at the small business I thought I might want to grow for my future. That business served me well for a few years. It gave me more time and flexibility as a single mom. When a full-time salaried job with benefits came along, I was ready to set aside my business and take the security of a new opportunity.

I had to learn to approach life with humility and a teachable spirit. I believe in being open to learning new things through other people and our circumstances.

I recall a song that really spoke to me during my healing process. The good news is that our scars and heartaches don't have to define us or destroy us.

*"Heal the Wound"*
*by Point of Grace*

*I used to dream that I could rewrite history*
*I used to dream that each mistake could be erased*
*Then I could just pretend*
*I never knew the me back then*

*I used to pray that you would take this shame away*
*Hide all the evidence of who I've been*
*But it's the memory of*
*The place you brought me from*
*That keeps me on my knees*
*And even though I'm free*

*Heal the wound but leave the scar*
*A reminder of how merciful you are*
*I am broken, torn apart*
*Take the pieces of this heart*
*And heal the wound but leave the scar*

*I have not lived a life that boasts of anything*
*I don't take pride in what I bring*
*But I'll build an altar with*
*The rubble that you've found me in*
*And every stone will sing*
*Of what you can redeem*

*Heal the wound but leave the scar*
*A reminder of how merciful you are*
*I am broken, torn apart*
*Take the pieces of this heart*
*And heal the wound but leave the scar*

*Don't let me forget*
*Everything you've done for me*
*Don't let me forget*
*The beauty in the suffering*

*Heal the wound but leave the scar*
*A reminder of how merciful you are*
*I am broken, torn apart*
*Take the pieces of this heart*
*And heal the wound but leave the scar*

I really relate to the words in the chorus of this song and also the phrase, "Don't let me forget the beauty in the suffering." Pain is a teacher if we're open to the lesson. Most of us have been broken at some point and have some scars from life. Those scars have changed me. How could they not? I have grown in ways I never would have otherwise. I learned that those scars are a part of my life statement. They have helped me become my authentic self as I opened myself up for growth. I came to find what mattered to me at this stage of life and was more comfortable with telling someone what I needed from them, and asking what they needed too. I got comfortable being vulnerable with others and sharing from my heart when I thought it might encourage someone else in their life. I didn't feel the need to try to impress someone. It was more about a deeper level of connection and acceptance of others.

I learned that emotional pain could be worse than physical pain, but that you will survive. Many days, my heart ached so bad that I just wanted to give up. I felt that I couldn't take it any longer, but each day, I had just enough hope and strength from God to keep taking one step after another. I also knew that I had to be there for my children. They were counting on me and needed me.

I learned that I had to take care of myself physically and emotionally, no matter what happened to me in life. No one else could do that for me. At first, I felt selfish, and then I realized that it was irresponsible to neglect self-care. Many people take better care of their cars than they do their own physical and emotional health.

I realized that each day came with both blessings and challenges. Understanding that every day will have some hassles makes it easier to just deal with them and move on. But take your time to notice the blessings that come each day too. For me, nature is such a powerful sign of God's involvement with his creation. I love to observe the sky for its changing panorama. One day it's the cloud formation. Another day it's the sunrise or sunset. Don't become callous to the beauty that surrounds you.

Forgive others. We all have people in our lives that irritate us and occasionally do really stupid things. When offended, try to let them off the hook so that you don't end up with a toxic heart. It may not be emotionally healthy for you to be real close to them, but let it go so that you can still enjoy a casual relationship with them.

Don't always trust your emotions. They will fluctuate and you may find yourself making some poor decisions if you do so when you're emotionally charged. I find that I need to be quiet more these days and pray about things that bother me and then address them as I gain more clarity about the situation.

And one of the best things I've learned with the yuck of life is that, "This too will pass." Nothing seems to last forever. Usually some other challenge arises as another leaves. For me, understanding that helps me to handle things better.

### Personal Application – Step 1

1. Have you experienced personal growth out of the hard times in your life? What did you learn from it and what were some of your healthy coping mechanisms? Are there negative coping mechanisms you need to let go of?

2. If you were to face that situation again, or something similar, would you do anything differently?

3. Could what you have learned in your hard time help someone else that is currently experiencing it? Are you willing to be vulnerable with your story if it means helping another person along the way?

# Human Resilience

## CHAPTER THREE - STEP 2

*"WE CANNOT WRITE IN WATER. WE CANNOT CARVE IN WATER. WATER'S NATURE IS TO FLOW AND THAT IS HOW WE SHOULD TREAT LIFE…EMOTION, NEGATIVE OR POSITIVE. DO NOT DENY IT BUT ALWAYS LET IT FLOW THROUGH AND THEN AWAY."*

*-ANONYMOUS*

It was time for me to adapt to my new reality and to start planning for my future. I had learned so much already and I now had more of my old strength and confidence back. I finally acknowledged that regardless of how I felt about my situation, I was the only one who could improve it. That is the power of human resilience.

Resilience isn't something that you are either born with or not. It is something that can be learned and developed in anyone by changing behaviors, thoughts and actions over time. We have to own our emotions. I think of resilience as a sort of psychological fitness. In the same way we need to exercise to be physically fit, we also have to be willing to do things differently to change our outlook and improve our emotional wellness. I found myself taking small steps that included adjusting my attitude and forgiving others, for my own emotional wellness.

When I found myself overthinking past conversations or negative situations, I felt worse. Meditating on positive affirmations was helpful for me. It might have been an empowering quote that was relative to my struggle, or maybe it was a scripture verse that was more hope-filled. I had to let go of the negative thoughts. Having gone through the heartache of divorce made it easier for me to fall into negative thought patterns. I would question myself over and over. I had to remember my abilities from before the divorce and call upon those personal strengths to rebuild my future positively. I had to remind myself of the coping skills that had helped me in the past, such as thinking the best of others.

I also found that setting goals for myself was helpful. There was so much that I wanted to accomplish that it would have been overwhelming if I didn't just focus on a few things at a time. What could I accomplish in one month, or three months? What should I begin thinking about for six months and then a year? Sketching some possibilities out was both empowering and exciting. I wanted to go back to school eventually. My first degree was in alternative medicine and the credits would not transfer into a master's degree, even though I had done all the work and used the knowledge in my job every day.

It was an ominous task to think of starting all over again with another bachelor's degree so that I could accomplish my goal of a master's degree. I could have been easily defeated with thoughts of being too old to start school again. However, I recall being at a conference held by the school where I completed my holistic nutrition degree. The keynote speaker was a seventy-five year old black woman that had just completed her PhD there. She said it had been a long road, but she realized that whether she completed the degree or not, that she would still be seventy-five in the three years it took her to earn it. I thought to myself, if a woman in her seventies can have that kind of attitude, surely I could do it. And I did. It was a few years before I could start but I set my intention towards that and started part time. Eventually, I finished through an accelerated adult program that allowed me to continue working full time. I graduated Summa Cum Laude with a B.S. in psychology. That gave me what I needed to go after my ultimate goal of earning my master's. I applied and was accepted into the program. I'll graduate with my M.S. in exercise science and health promotion: Wellness Coaching in 2016. It's never too late to go after your dreams.

If you don't know what you should do next, take some time for your own self- discovery. Do some brainstorming on things that might interest you. Don't worry about what could keep it from happening right now, like finances or time. Just get it on paper. I have learned that if there's a determined will, you will find a way. Adjusting your attitude from a negative mindset that tells you it will never happen to one of considering possibilities is key.

Chuck Swindoll speaks about how much our attitude affects our lives. He believes that "life is 10% what happens to us and 90% how we respond to it." Once you understand how much power this belief gives you, you understand when he goes on to say, "I believe the single most significant decision I can make on a day-to-day basis is my choice of attitude. Attitude keeps me going or cripples my progress. It alone fuels my fire or assaults my hope. You can choose how you will think about any circumstance, event or relationship in your life. Ask—is this the way I want to think and live?"

If I want to experience life from a positive place emotionally, I have to choose it daily. Positivity is one of the secrets to becoming resilient. Letting go of the negative feelings you have towards situations and people frees you up. Negativity can be toxic to your emotional and physical health. Are you allowing negative thoughts to take up space in your head rent free? Are those negative thoughts helping you to be a better person? Consider a gratitude journal where you write out three things every day that you're thankful for. That helped me to remember the good in my life while I was struggling with the hard stuff. There's always something we can do to improve our situation, even if it seems insignificant. Little things add up to noticeable change over time.

I believe that changing my attitude included getting better at forgiving those who had hurt or offended me. I believe that forgiveness is another important healing tool that can help you deal with both traumatic events and day-to-day problems. Hanging on to offenses can keep you in emotional bondage. Forgiving people who have hurt or offended you is more for yourself than it is for them. When we don't forgive someone, it's kind of like drinking poison and hoping the offender dies. They may not have a clue how you're feeling. They may be perfectly content in their life and totally unaffected. I strive to live at peace with others in my life as much as possible. It just feels better inside my own heart. As we learn to forgive and adapt to the hard things in life, we free ourselves. That doesn't mean that what someone may have done to you is okay. And it doesn't mean you have to be close to them and pretend they didn't hurt you. However, you are just choosing to let it go. It also makes it easier to be around those people going forward.

Try thinking the best of others. You don't know the burdens they are carrying in their hearts. Think about how you want others to treat you when you mess up. Humans will fail each other. It's inevitable. Be gentle with others and kind to yourself.

I also had to forgive myself. I felt like I had let my kids down by not being as good at single parenting as I would have hoped to be. I had to let that go and trust that God would fill in the gaps.

I discovered how much I needed quality relationships in my life. I needed people that I could connect to on a deeper, real level. I found that the people I enjoyed conversation with the most were not necessarily those who were just like me. I found people who were totally engaged in our conversation to be the most appealing. They didn't feel the need to do all the talking. It was a good balance and they really cared about what I had to say too. It's easy to tell if someone is just waiting for you to finish speaking so they can talk versus the person that genuinely cares and looks you in the eye. They respond to what you've said like it matters. They show, by their comments and questions, that what you have to say is worth listening to and discussing. I found myself gravitating toward the people who were real and cared about my thoughts and feelings. You will feel so much more supported when you are in the company of someone that practices good communication skills. You will also deepen the intimacy level in that relationship.

Carl Rogers built his client-centered therapy style based on good reflective listening skills and the understanding that the client is an expert in their own life. It is rare today to find someone that will take the time to look you in the eye and really try to understand both what you are saying and, more importantly, what you're not saying. Rogers states, "It is astonishing how elements that seem insoluble become soluble when someone listens, how confusions that seem irremediable turn into relatively clear flowing streams when one is heard. I have deeply appreciated the times that I have experienced this sensitive, empathetic, concentrated listening." I have a few people in my life that are skilled in the art of listening and I count them as major blessings. They are the people that know me the best.

As Carl Roger's stated, part of being someone's support system is being a good listener. Practice reflecting back what you heard the other person say. It may not be what they meant at all. Allow them to clarify if they were misunderstood. Ask questions about what they are talking about. Give them your full attention by looking at them. If you want to deepen the relationships in your life, try these skills and see what kind of response you get. I believe it's something we all should be working on.

As we seek to build resilience, we have to realize that we are all distinct individuals and different strategies will work for some and not for others. Most of us need some kind of support system in tough times as well as day-to-day to make life more enjoyable. For some, that may come from faith based organizations. For others, it will be one close friend or a civic group. Another person may feel more connected when they serve others. Try different support strategies until you find what works best for you. I know that for me, I'd be lost without a few close girlfriends that really get me and know me at that deeper, heart level.

Another helpful thing to tell yourself to build resilience is that it won't always be this way. It may feel like it today, but I have seen, time and time again, that situations resolve and life goes on. I really like what the serenity prayer says. "God grant me the ability to accept the things I cannot change, courage to change what I can, and wisdom to know the difference." That can help add some perspective to your situation.

Try to look at the events in your life as opportunities for growth. You may find that your current struggle may bring about something you could never have imagined otherwise. Is there something hidden deep inside your heart that you'd love to do but never got around to? For me, it was writing this book. I talked about writing a book about fifteen years ago. If I had written it then, it would have been a totally different book. Sharing my story now is attached to helping others recreate their own lives. It's about helping women get healthy in their body, soul and spirit. I never would have chosen to be divorced, but it happened. Now I can understand how incredibly difficult a divorce can be and all the emotions that are attached to it. I have experienced life to be a journey that is filled with both blessings and challenges. We can learn and grow from both.

A common thread through all of these resilience building strategies is the need to keep things in perspective. Try not to blow things out of proportion and remember that nothing lasts forever. It may look difficult today, but it doesn't have to stay that way. Journaling is another tool that can help you find clarity in your situation. I found that as I wrote out my thoughts and really pondered them, that the direction I needed to take became clearer. Try to find the balance between letting yourself feel your strong emotions and knowing when it's time to focus on something else, like a work project, to help you function normally. There is hope for tomorrow and a better future is likely ahead of you.

Recent research has found human resilience in the most unlikely of places. The latest research coming from the field of positive psychology has found that there can be great growth following trauma in patients diagnosed with Post Traumatic Stress Disorder (PTSD). This is referred to as Post Traumatic Growth (PTG). For example, two people experience the trauma of war. When they return, one may get stuck in a deep depression from all they witnessed in that horrific setting. They may get stuck in this place and be consumed with negative thoughts regarding all the atrocities in the world. The other may go through a time of depression and adjustment as well, but then take a different perspective. Perhaps they become grateful that their life was spared and see it as a transition point to achieve something meaningful with the rest of their years. Research found that what makes the difference between these two people is the level of optimism a person possessed prior to the stressful event.

Martin E.P. Seligman talks about working with the U.S. Army to teach their leaders resilience skills, as noted in an article in the Harvard Business Review. The goal was to reduce the number of soldiers that will experience PTSD by teaching them optimism and coping skills before combat occurs. Prior focus was limited to getting the soldiers physically fit. This study was used to help them develop coping skills before a war setting that would make them psychologically fit for battle and life afterwards.

Soldiers in the program take the Global Assessment Tool (GAT), which measures strengths instead of weaknesses, in the following areas: emotional, family, social, and spiritual fitness. Then, they take online trainings in their areas of weakness to better prepare themselves for any possible trauma. This type of training could also translate well into the corporate world where learned optimism could greatly enhance a leader's ability to manage teams of people. This hypothesis is being tested on a grand scale with the U.S. Army. It will be very interesting to watch for the results of this mental resilience training over time.

I think this is very interesting stuff. Focusing on optimism instead of negativity affects us psychologically. Knowing the research shows that we can come out better and stronger after trauma should be an encouragement.

We have the ability to change our perspective. What we think about really matters for our emotional health.

Philippians 4:8, "Finally, brothers and sisters, whatever is true, whatever is noble, whatever is right, whatever is pure, whatever is lovely, whatever is admirable, if anything is excellent or praiseworthy, think about such things."

### Personal Application – Step 2

1. What would you like to be different in your life in the next year?

2. Are there people in your life that you need to forgive so that you can be free in your heart?

3. Do you currently have a good support system where you feel heard and understood? (This could include friends, a counselor, family, a support group, etc.)

4. What has helped you to feel more hopeful in the past?

5. What have you learned about yourself during hard times?

# Growth in Change

## CHAPTER FOUR - STEP 3

*"LIFE IS CHANGE. GROWTH IS OPTIONAL. CHOOSE WISELY."*

*-KAREN KAISER CLARK*

Change is an inevitable part of life. Most of us fight it. Sometimes you have to force yourself to do what you can to change your situation when life seems unfair. I had to tell myself that my life wasn't over. It was just different. In time, I was able to get comfortable with the unknown.

I had to redefine myself as a single person with an unknown future. The reality is that none of us truly know our future. It's wise to plan, but things happen in life that are out of our control. Once I accepted that my future would look different, I was able to start discovering what a new normal would look like. That was hard because we had been a family with certain traditions for twenty-four years. I had to tell myself, again and again, that many people have faced this and that I could too. I was never going to like what the divorce did to our family, but I could choose to accept it and to do my best to make new traditions. It was okay to grieve that loss, but I had to understand and accept that I could only control so much in life. What other people choose and many situations are out of your control.

Even if you didn't choose the changes that have come into your life, you are still the only one that can decide what your attitude will be in response. During the darkest of my days, I kept a gratitude journal. Each night, I recorded three things that I was grateful for. Some days it was a challenge, but it taught me to be thankful for the little, daily blessings that I still had in my life, like my children and a place to live and great friends. A gratitude journal can benefit you throughout your life, but can be especially cathartic during days when you need to consciously look for the good.

Unexpected change can bring about growth that would not have happened in any other way. I don't know if I would have put so much time and energy into more education in my field if I hadn't had to build a new career. In some ways, that turned out to be a blessing. I have met and worked with so many wonderful people that I never would have met if my situation hadn't changed. That was a blessing that came out of a bad situation. I love what I do and I love the difference I can make in another person's life and health. I think this quote by Ram Dass is profound:

*"Without change, something sleeps inside us, and seldom awakens. The sleeper must awaken. Healing does not mean going back to the way things were before, but rather allowing what is now to move us closer to God."*

Expect it to take time to accept change, especially change that you did not want. Learning to accept oneself in a new situation is also a process. You need to be honest with yourself. What needs to change to get what you want and need for your future? Have faith in your abilities. Make a list of what you're good at. Then, decide what is important to you and go after it. Do the hard work now so that you can become your best you. For me, it was going back and getting another degree, along with many certifications in the field of health and wellness. Now, I'm working on my master's degree with the hope of being able to teach in my field at the college level part time. Being able to positively impact someone that wants to work in wellness gives me a real sense of satisfaction. I love being able to mentor others. I never would have thought that I'd be helping to guide young professionals in their careers, but it happened several times in my last job. Don't give up on the things that excite you. What would give your life more meaning and purpose that you could be working on now?

As much as possible, seek to keep the past in the past. You can't change history. It will always be a part of you. But you can make peace with it for your emotional health. I try to live by the motto, "Cherish yesterday. Live today. Dream tomorrow."

I will never forget that I had a wonderful marriage and family life for twenty-four years. I feel very thankful for that. Today, I am happy again with a new husband and step children that are wonderful to me. I have a full life. My children are all grown and finding their callings in life. I try to be more fully present in my day-to-day activities and relationships. Tomorrow, I will achieve the goals that I'm working on today. I think it's a healthy place to be emotionally.

If you find yourself engaging in negative self-talk, try a new approach.

Quit telling yourself what you can't do. Focus on what you can do and build on that. You have to learn to believe in your abilities and to go after what you want for your future. Henry Ford said it best. "Whether you think you can, or that you can't, you are usually right." You are responsible for yourself and you are the only one who can change your future. Just because you haven't done something in the past doesn't mean that you can't do it now. Find the right tools to support you. What are your dreams? You get to choose.

Be careful what you choose to think about. Keep it positive. Put yourself around people that will encourage you to be your best. We tend to become like the people we hang out with, so choose people that are healthy and will inspire you to be your best. I tell coaching clients that if they want different results, they will need to do different things. It's not as difficult as you might think. Just take the first step forward, and then another.

When you accept, embrace and learn from change, you will find yourself getting stronger each day. Future challenges won't seem as monumental when you put them in the right perspective. You will only find out how strong you are when that is your only choice. Do you have a life mission statement? I do and I would encourage you to consider one. Here's mine:

*"I want to be a positive role model for faith, health, compassion, and show love and kindness to all the people I have the privilege of working with or being in a relationship with."*

I believe that success stems from taking small, intentional steps forward in the direction of our dreams. If you don't like how your life is going right now, take steps that will propel you forward into something that excites you and adds meaning to your days. Work with a coach if some accountability would help you reach your dreams. I have worked with a few along the way and they have really helped me stay accountable to my goals, and even discover additional dreams.

Understand that growth isn't linear. It's two steps forward and three steps back sometimes. At other times, you may take several leaps forward. It can be a messy, challenging, frustrating, time consuming process, but it also gives our days purpose. It's worth the effort. There were many times when I felt confused and wondered if I was off track, but I kept plugging away and, over time, so many great things began to happen. My confidence grew and so did my job opportunities.

Discover who you are today as an individual, not just how you had previously been defined. What part of yourself or your life did you put on hold? Are there things you regret not doing earlier in your life? Think back to a time in your life when you felt on fire. What were you doing differently then? What coping mechanisms did you apply then that might help you now? Let your heart dream again. You are capable of so much more than you can imagine.

If you're not sure of where to begin, go to my resource page at the back of the book and take the free signature strengths test. It will help you find your strengths and may offer help for your future.

## Personal Application – Step 3

1. Are there things in your life that you can't control and need to accept?

2. Is negative self-talk holding you back? Are you using negative coping mechanisms that are self-destructive?

3. Are there things that you might have put on hold in your life that you would like to do now?

4. What might you dare to dream for your future if you knew that you couldn't fail?

# Self-Care

## CHAPTER FIVE - STEP 4

*"WOMEN MUST COME OF AGE BY HERSELF. SHE MUST FIND HER CENTER ALONE."*

*-ANNE MORROW LINDBERG*

There was a time that I considered self-care as being selfish. I had a family to take care of. There were so many things on my to-do list that needed attention first. I had to suffer some physical issues around the time of my divorce before my doctor told me that I needed to make taking care of myself a higher priority.

I have eaten well and exercised all my life, but I totally neglected the little things that actually calmed my body and helped to restore me. Stress took its toll for a few years until I learned how to deal with it.

Today, I share with my clients the importance of making time for their health and self-care so they don't need to make time for illness.

## PHYSICAL SELF-CARE

*"THE GREATEST WEALTH IS HEALTH."*
*-VIRGIL*

Taking care of our health allows us to do the things that really matter to us. Having been a health coach, personal trainer, nutrition educator, and weight loss specialist for many years has shown me how much most people really do want to look and feel better. Most people just don't have a clue where to start. It's okay if you've made mistakes along the way. You can change your future starting today. You can achieve amazing transformations with small steps that really do add up to a changed life after some time.

I've helped hundreds of clients lose both small and large amounts of weight as well as to find ways to exercise that they can fit into their schedules. Almost everyone can do something. It's very important that the exercise is chosen appropriately for the individual, always considering their physical limitations. Too often, people try to do programs that are too intense for them and then they either get hurt or totally discouraged. They may be doing what someone else is doing or using a "cookie cutter" workout that doesn't consider their level of fitness. A well-educated trainer should always be able to tell you why they chose a particular exercise for you. A well-designed program should feel achievable, slightly challenging, empowering, energizing, and leave you feeling better and with more confidence.

I've worked in corporate settings with very busy professionals that think they don't have the time to take care of themselves. It's been fun to watch them gain back control of their lives as they learn to consistently focus on just one or two small changes at a time. Expect it to take several months to change and sustain new habits. You've probably invested many years into your old habits. Diets don't work and no one wants to live a life of deprivation. If you do just one thing better this week, and then add one more thing next week, and another small thing the following week, you will find yourself with new healthy habits in no time.

My goal is to help people learn to make better choices so they have the skills to maintain a healthier future for themselves. Most people will start to feel better after adding in some fruit and vegetables and reducing packaged food consumption. Simply start increasing water consumption and reduce the soda pop. Those simple steps will give you a great start to a healthier lifestyle.

When it comes to exercise, I take a very realistic position. If someone hasn't exercised for years or is carrying extra weight, it is very unrealistic that they're going to go to the gym six days a week. Putting on a pedometer and tracking their steps offers a greater chance of success for them. Walking strengthens the body, rejuvenates the mind and enlivens the spirit. Most people can handle walking. My new husband and I go out for a walk in the morning before work as much as possible. It's a great way to help get you to the recommended 10,000 steps per day. That is where I get most of my cardiovascular work without a lot of stress on my joints and we get time to connect as a couple. We vary our route to include hills some days and greater distance other days. Some days we add in walking lunges and push-ups against a railing on one of our routes. When we can't get outside, I will get on my treadmill or my indoor cycling bike. It's always good to have a backup plan.

It's important to make both cardiovascular and total body strength training part of your routine. If you only do cardio, you will not maintain lean muscle mass and it will be much harder for you to lose weight and keep it off. As you age, your body naturally gets softer and strength training is needed to maintain a toned and strong body.

Loss of functional strength accelerates the aging process and many will begin to lose height and start to slump over. Both my grandmother and my mother never lost even an inch of height as they aged. They did, however, get exercise regularly throughout their lives and eat nourishing foods that supported healthy bone structure. Think about how the choices you're making today may affect you down the road.

Strength training doesn't have to be ridiculously intense to have value. You just need to work all of your major muscle groups a few times per week at an intensity that will build some actual muscle. You can accomplish this in 20-30 minutes per session for basic functional strength. I have found strength training to be the best way to improve a person's body composition and functional ability. If you want your clothes to fit better, pick up some weights that challenge your muscles. If you are not familiar with weights, get the assistance of a personal trainer. Learning proper form is key to prevent injury.

I became a huge believer in yoga when I was the program manager for the Medtronic Wellness Centers (a Fortune 500 company in Minneapolis). Not only did I notice that yoga helped runners lessen injuries by maintaining flexibility, but it also helped people to manage their stressful jobs. I went on for more training while working that account and by the time I had my 200-hour certification done, I was a committed believer. Even fifteen minutes of yoga a few times a week is helpful.

As we age, we naturally begin to lose balance, strength and flexibility if we don't take steps to slow that process down. Yoga will help you improve your posture. Years of sitting in front of a computer take a toll on how you carry yourself. Yoga will also help you learn how to slow down and calm your stressors through breath work and intentional movement.

Yoga can be done as a more physically intense practice that will help build lean muscle while stretching your body to minimize injuries from other forms of exercise.

Restorative yoga can be very helpful for deep relaxation and greater help with flexibility since the poses are held longer and props are normally used to aid in getting into the positions.

Most adults are very shallow breathers. We need to learn to slow down and breathe deeper. Yoga is where I learned to breathe at this deeper level. Over time, I noticed that I was calmer in my day-to-day activities. I also noticed that I was more patient and could refrain from negative responses better when dealing with conflict.

All forms of exercise should be taught with the emphasis of learning to listen to your body. Proper form and technique should always come before intensity. In yoga, you connect the breath to the movement, which helps you to get to know your body better. If you feel pain in a yoga pose, you should be taught to pull back out a bit and find the place you can do it with ease to avoid hurting your body. You will also learn to notice when to push yourself a bit as well.

When you exercise with good form and technique, you get to know your body better, what works for you, and when your body is trying to tell you that something isn't quite right. I had a Medtronic employee that used to attend my classes tell me that one day, he was home taking a shower and knew something didn't feel quite right with his heart. At first, he wanted to deny it. Then, he said he heard me saying, "Listen to your body," in his head. He also felt a small breeze on his shower curtain when there shouldn't have been any breeze. Because he had learned to notice when something didn't feel right, he finally made the call to 911 and, that same day, had a heart stent put in. Learning to listen to his body literally saved his life.

Pick an exercise that you enjoy. If you like to dance, try Zumba or Hip-Hop. If your joints hurt, try swimming or water aerobics. A group fitness class, taught by a qualified instructor, can make exercise a lot more fun. A good instructor will offer lots of modification to keep the class safe for everyone. I sometimes use DVD's at home to push myself or for variety. Try some different things until you find what works for you.

If you have a goal of gaining strength or losing weight, you will need to change your routine up. As your body gets used to a routine, you will no longer get the same results. A change in routine is suggested about every six weeks. If you're involved with group fitness classes, your instructor should be providing you enough variety for continued progress.

If you still need a push to get you started exercising, consider the fact that physical exercise is associated with disease prevention. Dr. Vonda Wright studies aging athletes and has found that exercise helps prevent diseases such as diabetes, hypertension, heart disease, and even some cancers. "Numerous studies reveal that exercise targets many aspects of brain function and has broad effects on overall brain health, learning, memory, and depression, particularly in older populations. Moreover, regular exercise can protect against several types of dementia (e.g. Alzheimer's disease) and certain types of brain injury (e.g. stroke)," (Powers & Howley, 2012). Regular aerobic exercise has been found to be the most supportive by promoting brain growth factor to help enhance learning and memory. Exercise also reduces inflammation, hypertension and insulin resistance, which are very common as people age. My mother has Alzheimer's and my grandmother had some form of dementia. I am highly motivated to keep exercising to maintain good brain health.

Stress is a part of all of our lives and can affect us negatively or positively. The danger comes when we perceive it as negative. I know that stress played a big part in negative things happening in my body physically when I was going through my divorce. The symptoms I experienced included headaches, difficulty sleeping and staying asleep, chronic fatigue, loss of appetite, lack of concentration and focus, memory problems, anxiety and irritability. I hardly slept for the first nine months after Doug moved out and I developed a cyst that was tested for cancer. I was told that I needed to learn to manage my stress for my health's sake. I was not dealing with my situation well.

There have been times where stress has been positive for me, such as when I got extra busy because I was working on a goal that really mattered to me. The American Psychological Association considers small doses of stressors that motivate you to get something done as being positive.

While working at Orbital/ATK, I offered a fifteen minute mindfulness stretch break twice per week. Employees were able to come to a dimly lit fitness room with quiet yoga music in the background. They didn't have to change their clothes and it only took a few minutes. We would start with a few minutes of breath work, then move into stretching, and then end with a few more minutes of quiet breathing. These brief bouts of quiet meditation can help to calm your body and leave you refreshed for the rest of the day.

Other ideas you may want to try to help relieve stress include:

- Quit worrying about things you can't control.
- Take care of the easy things on your to-do list to minimize the feeling of being overwhelmed.

- Prepare well for situations you know cause you anxiety, such as job interviews or presentations.
- Do your best to resolve conflicts with others.
- Set realistic goals and don't overschedule yourself.
- Eat regular, healthy meals.
- Allow for 7-8 hours of sleep each night.
- Try meditation.
- Exercise.
- Make time to check-in with your friends, even if it's just a text on busy days.
- Try to see the humor in situations. Laugh more often.
- Give up bad habits like excessive alcohol, cigarettes and caffeine.
- Plan ahead so you're not always running late.
- Take some time to get organized so you limit wasting time trying to find things.
- Help someone in need.

## SPIRITUAL SELF-CARE

*"COME TO ME, ALL YOU WHO ARE WEARY AND BURDENED,
AND I WILL GIVE YOU REST."
-MATTHEW 11:28*

We were created as spiritual beings. For me, making time at the start of each day for some inspirational reading is a high priority. It's so easy to just go about your day and to neglect feeding your spirit. When we do this, we can feel empty and out of sorts. Reading and meditating on inspirational passages can be a very important part of your self-care. Here is a meditation mantra that I've used in the past. "I draw from the wellspring of my heavenly father for my creativity." And at other times I'll use breath work to center me. I've used the following mantras:

- Inhale – Father God,
- Exhale – I belong to you.
Or
- Inhale – Be still
- Exhale – and know
- Inhale – that I
- Exhale – am God.

Pick a mantra that feeds your soul and then practice saying it during deep breathing exercises. You should notice a wonderful calming feeling afterwards.

Joshua Becker, from BecomingaMinimalist.com, states, "Silence quietly calls for our attention. Because only in extended periods of solitude can we rediscover our hearts and the voice of timeless wisdom in our lives." The constant noise around us can be a distraction at times and can keep us from hearing the messages we need in life. Even taking five minutes in the morning to sit quietly and do some breathing can change the trajectory of your day. I also love to sit on the deck or go for a walk and enjoy the sounds of nature. Times of silence really nourish my soul.

If you are a faith-minded person and you struggle with negative self-talk or have experienced mild depression in the past, you may want to give centering prayer a try. Centering prayer, developed by a monk named Thomas Merton, has been tested against mindfulness-based cognitive therapy to help prevent depression relapses with very promising results. Both teach a person the importance of being fully present, right now. That's a key concept in all mindfulness and meditation practices. In an article in the Journal of Religious Health, J. Knabb writes, "[Centering prayer] allows the individual to get in touch with his or her center of being…is an effortless form of prayer with God in the present moment…and helps the individual to relate differently to his or her thoughts."

I think the key of centering prayer is how it gets a person to slow down long enough to hear the messages inside of them. Most of us are constantly being bombarded with work and noise and it can be difficult to find time to reflect on the truly important things in life. I know that I need time alone and in quietness to be better with others. For a person of faith, centering prayer may be something you want to try for your spiritual and emotional health.

## SELF-NURTURE

*"THE ONE WHO FOLLOWS THE CROWD WILL USUALLY GET NO FURTHER THAN THE CROWD. THE ONE WHO WALKS ALONE IS LIKELY TO FIND HIMSELF IN PLACES NO ONE HAS EVER BEEN."*
*-ALBERT EINSTEIN*

It's important to be healthy on your own before you seek out romantic relationships. The self-assurance that you are okay all by yourself is something that no one can take away from you. That gives you amazing freedom to just live life the way it is meant to be lived without all of the confusion created by fear and worry about what someone else might, or might not, be doing. It is best if they are a part of your life because you choose them to be—not because you can't survive without them. What a difference!

I think it's more common than not for people to enter a new relationship right away after a divorce. Your confidence has been diminished and you need to be around people that help you feel better again. I dated someone a few months after my divorce proceedings started. He was a really nice guy but it was too soon. I think it would have been better for me just to focus on my kids, myself, and my girlfriends.

Meaningful relationships add so much to the quality of a person's life. Spend time with people that care about how you are feeling and what you have to say. Conversation should be mutually satisfying and not dominated by one party. Make time to really connect and nurture quality relationships. Notice how much better you feel after you've had a good belly laugh. I've had friends going through cancer treatment that were advised to watch comedies to help lighten their spirits.

If you're not in a relationship right now, that's okay. Take good care of yourself and follow your heart. Use this time to discover what you want to do next.

It's important to stay mentally and intellectually sharp. Ask yourself if you are currently growing or stagnating intellectually. We should never quit learning. Are you doing things to grow your career? Do you need additional schooling to reach your goals in life? We should all be involving ourselves in intellectually stimulating activities like reading quality books, doing puzzles or playing strategy games, and learning new things. What might you like to learn about? Maybe you'd enjoy taking a painting class. I started listening to books on CD while I'm driving, or teaching tapes. There are so many creative ways to learn new things.

Become your own best friend. I believe that we should find ways to enjoy our own company. Maybe it's more reading, or eating exactly what you want for dinner on occasion. Maybe it's an activity you want to do more. Find out what brings you joy and satisfaction at this point in your life. It doesn't have to be something big. I love to sit in my comfy recliner with a cup of coffee in the morning and read before the day begins. At night, a bubble bath with a candle can bring about the same feeling. You don't have to be running all the time to have life satisfaction. Joyce Saunders once said, "There's a difference between being grounded and being run into the ground. Some things keep you rooted and some just weigh you down, and you have to decide what you'd rather keep around." I think that's a powerful statement to consider as you look at what matters most to you in life. You really can't do it all. We all have to make choices as to what we want in our lives to be happy and healthy.

Here are some ideas to help you nurture yourself:

- Keep a gratitude journal. Every day, write down three things you're grateful for as a way to help you be more thankful for the blessings you have in your life.
- Learn to say, "No." Say, "Yes," to the things that matter to you and let go of the things that aren't a good fit for your skills.
- Eat healthy meals and snacks. When you fuel your body with healthy foods, you will look better, feel better and have more energy.
- Unplug from as many electronics as possible for a full day sometime.
- Journal your thoughts. Writing them out can help bring clarity to a situation you're not sure about.
- Go to the beach or another place in nature so you can experience some natural beauty.
- Catch up with an old friend. Make social gatherings a part of your calendar.
- Watch a funny movie when you're feeling lonely to lift your spirits.
- Get rid of the clutter in your home environment. Open spaces can help you feel calmer.
- Take a yoga class. Yoga is a mind-body-spirit workout that can help you to feel centered.
- Go to the park and watch some little kids play and experience their laughter.
- Drink lots of water. Sometimes, when you feel really fatigued, all you really need to do is rehydrate your body for some renewed energy.
- Experiment with different types of teas. You can enjoy them hot or iced.
- Listen to a personal development CD or webinar.
- Go dancing with friends.
- Create a vision board on a big poster board. Cut out pictures of things you want to be a part of your life. Dream and have fun with it.

## Personal Application – Step 4

1. Is anything currently weighing you down emotionally that you need to let go of?

2. Are you getting regular physical exercise? If not, what might you see yourself doing?

3. Have you thought about your life purpose? What could you do to nurture your spirit?

4. What do you feel is missing in your life that you'd like to work on?

# Thriving

## CHAPTER SIX - STEP 5

*"GO CONFIDENTLY IN THE DIRECTION OF YOUR DREAMS!*
*LIVE THE LIFE YOU'VE IMAGINED."*

*-HENRY DAVID THOREAU*

Does the concept of thriving feel empowering to you? Or does it sound like something out of reach at this point in your life? Have you been merely surviving for far too long? The fact that you are reading this book tells me that you are ready to at least begin making some positive changes for your future.

I believe that a thriving life is not a perfect life. It does, however, mean that you are making steady progress with the things that matter to you. There's growth and positive development in your life when you are flourishing.

For me, thriving means that I'm living my life intentionally and accomplishing things that matter to me. What is it that matters to you that you have yet to accomplish? It's not too late and no dream is too big. Breaking your goals down into manageable steps is your starting point. Before you know it, you will have reached your goal.

You may be thriving in some areas of your life but not in others. I encourage you to consider what changes you may need to make to bring your life into balance. I also encourage you to set some goals that will help you reach your potential. Maybe you need to hire a coach to help you figure that out. Life is not just about the end result, it's more about who you become in the process of reaching your goals.

The five key pillars associated with wellbeing that Rath & Harter (2010) researched in their book, Wellbeing: The Five Essential Elements, include:

- Career wellbeing
- Social wellbeing
- Financial wellbeing
- Physical wellbeing
- Community wellbeing

They believe that thriving comes when we are achieving balance in these five areas of our lives. Their research demonstrated that "66% of people are doing well in at least one of these areas, and just 7% are thriving in all five." Our wellbeing is affected when we are out of balance. You are the only one that can change your future for better days, months and years ahead. Start thinking about what area you would like to start with.

Finding your purpose, or key motivator, is very important. How we spend our time should be an indicator of what we value. My faith and my desire to help women are my key motivators. For me, empowering women to feel better about themselves isn't just a job. I believe it is a large part of my purpose and mission in life.

I encourage others to make the most of the life they're given, as I do the same. I am very much a work in progress, but I know where I want to go. I'm a huge believer in setting goals and achieving them. Ask yourself, what are you passionate about? What really motivates you?

## *CAREER WELLBEING*

*"FIND SOMETHING YOU'RE PASSIONATE ABOUT AND KEEP TREMENDOUSLY INTERESTED IN IT."*
*-JULIA CHILD*

The first element of wellbeing involves where we spend the bulk of our time. Do you feel stagnant or do you feel challenged in your career? Do you love what you do or is it hard to get up and go to work each day? Should you be looking for different work or should you learn to love your current job? Sometimes, changing your attitude towards what you are doing can make all the difference. Maybe trying a different approach would be more effective when dealing with your manager. Maybe you would like to do something completely different but feel it is not possible right now. Consider what makes the most sense for you at this time. Working with a coach or a career counselor may be helpful for you as well.

Try to find ways to use your strengths at work. Sure, you have to handle things you don't enjoy, but maybe you could work with your teams in a slightly different capacity. More is accomplished when teams function by utilizing each person's strengths. It can be helpful to go through the Myers-Briggs personality inventory to understand your psychological type. I found that understanding my team's personality style helped us to function more seamlessly.

Do you have a friend at work? Working side-by-side with pleasant people will also add joy to your job. You may need to find someone in another department if you are not connecting with any direct co-workers. Are there things you could be doing with your co-workers that would make your days more fun? Find out if your company offers any kind of wellness programming. Taking a lunchtime fitness class, joining a company golf league, or simply walking at lunch with a co-worker can meet both social and physical needs.

Have you ever considered trying to find someone to mentor you, or being a mentor to someone else? The mentor-mentee relationship can be very beneficial for both parties. It is relationship oriented and focuses on personal and professional development. It can be a great way to enhance your career and life satisfaction.

Sometimes we end up in difficult work situations and the only option is to look elsewhere. Maybe you need to go back to school or get some additional training so that you can apply for a better job. Consider how many years you may work and take steps that bring you to the place where your work is both challenging and meaningful. Many of us will be working much later in life, either by choice or financial necessity. It's never too late to go back to school to do something that will improve your situation.

## *SOCIAL WELLBEING*

*"LET US BE GRATEFUL TO PEOPLE WHO MAKE US HAPPY.*
*THEY ARE THE CHARMING GARDENERS WHO MAKE OUR SOULS BLOSSOM."*
*-MARCEL PROUST*

Having quality relationships in life can be one of the most fulfilling aspects in your journey. Do you have people you can count on to be there for you in life? If you do, don't neglect taking time to nurture those relationships. Good relationships are gifts in life. Sometimes we don't realize that until we are much older when we begin to feel the need for deeper connections with others. The people we love and care about are what make life worthwhile on so many levels.

Be open to learning what other people can teach you. You may not always see eye-to-eye with another person, but you can learn from every encounter if you are teachable. I have friends from many different backgrounds and interests. Being around people that aren't just like you keeps things interesting. For example, when I was working as a personal trainer and nutrition educator at a local gym, I trained women of all ages. As a trainer, you get to know your clients well, and quite often they become friends. At the time, these women ranged from about 27–55 years old. Our lives and histories were very different but we became the G-Force, which stood for Good Girls Gone Grape. Once a month, we met at someone's house and brought a bottle of wine and an appetizer. We met regularly for several years and became good friends in spite of our differences. Our lives have taken some of us in different directions ten years later, but most of those friendships remain on some level. One of the women in our group died too young from a rare stomach cancer. We were all there to support each other at the funeral. Be open to new relationships in places you would not have expected.

Show kindness to the people you encounter in life. Everyone you meet, regardless of what they show on the exterior, has some hurt or concern inside of them. I really try to make the people in my life feel loved, validated and heard. I mess up at times, but I really want to leave people feeling better after spending time with them.

One thing I found that made people feel validated was to find a way to include everyone in conversation in a small group setting. For example, when I had my team to my home for a Christmas party, I'd ask a question that required each person to share something about themselves. I might ask them, "What was the best thing that happened to you this past year?" Or, "If you could do anything with your life, what would that be?" So often, the extroverts dominate in a group and the introverts are never heard. Sometimes it's the quieter person that says something profound. I always got positive feedback with that and they came to expect it at gatherings. I think the greatest gift we can give another human being is that of being listened to and understood. That takes time and the willingness to be quiet and engage with others.

To bring about balance in this area of your life, you need to spend time engaging with others. Work is a great place to make friends and enjoy others. Strive to balance your social needs with work by blending them together.

Try sending a quick email, written note, or text to someone you love. You can make their day as you share something nice and say something sincere to them. Opening a hand written note that came in the mail is a rare and beautiful thing in today's world. Other times, it may be taking the time for a walk or a meal together. All relationships take some sacrifice in time and effort, but it is worth it.

Make a list of your family members and friends who you want to stay in contact with. With such busy lives today, we need to be intentional in connecting with the people we care about. I have some dear friends that I only see about once a year, but we treasure the friendships and have been able to maintain many of them for thirty years. Make it a priority to keep up with the people that love and care about you.

I try to share a meal with each of my grown kids once a month and to talk via phone with my son in Kansas. Sending texts can be a quick way to let someone know that you're thinking about them when you can't be together. Sending a card in the mail that can be read and reread is another way to make someone feel special. I have every card my kids have ever given me.

Doing something physical with another person is a way to blend both social and physical needs. My husband and I walk together most mornings. Occasionally, I'll meet a girlfriend for a walk around a city lake or at a yoga studio to take a class together. Consider what you like to do and find friends to join you.

Look for people that like to do positive things. You can be an encouragement to each other. Think about things you'd like to do more of in life and find people who are already doing it and see if you can join them. I've decided to start golfing and am taking some lessons with the plan to get involved with a women's league so that I can meet other women with the same interest. And, it's something active that I can do with my husband as well.

## FINANCIAL WELLBEING

*""WE MAKE A LIVING BY WHAT WE GET, BUT WE MAKE A LIFE BY WHAT WE GIVE."*
*-WINSTON CHURCHILL*

Some say that money can't buy happiness. Happiness will more likely come from having people we love in our lives and doing things that give our lives meaning.

However, having some financial security can lessen worry and anxiety over not having enough. Most of us have experienced financial concerns at some time in our lives and know the anxiety that too many bills and not enough money cause.

The peace of mind that comes from having a little cushion for a rainy day and some money invested for retirement enhances a person's wellbeing. It takes discipline to say no to things today so that you're able to handle the unexpected things later.

One way that I've seen money buy happiness is with travel. Whether it's a camping trip or an exotic destination, having the ability to get away from your day-to-day routine to a place that provides some rest and relaxation is good for your health and wellbeing. Seeing different parts of nature is soothing to the soul. Whether it's walking along the ocean in Florida or along the north shore of Lake Superior, I feel nurtured by different settings. I think it's more about getting away and being renewed in a different environment. Making memories with someone you care about is also a great way to nurture a relationship.

Happiness can also come from giving to others. When we invest in others with our time and/or our money, we can make a positive difference in their life. I like to give to organizations that I believe are making a difference. I also enjoy helping my adult children occasionally with things that help them to get established in life.

You don't have to be wealthy to improve your financial wellbeing. Start small and be faithful with setting something aside. If you have a 401K at work, take advantage of it, even if you just put a little in each paycheck. You will be surprised as you watch it grow over time. Your sense of financial wellbeing will increase as well.

Do you feel okay about your finances at this time? If not, maybe you should meet with a financial planner and get started by taking baby steps to increase your financial wellbeing. Every little bit adds up.

## *PHYSICAL WELLBEING*

*"IF I'D KNOWN I WAS GOING TO LIVE SO LONG, I'D HAVE
TAKEN BETTER CARE OF MYSELF."*
*-LEON ELDRED*

If you want to thrive in the area of physical wellbeing, you need to take care of your health. Think of your body like an expensive car. Would you neglect basic care of the car such as not changing the oil, rotating the tires, or ignoring warning lights? I doubt it. Many Americans are doing just that with their bodies. We don't get to "trade in" our bodies like we do with cars. You owe it to yourself to take good care of your body so it serves you well for life. How you eat, sleep and move all have both short and long term consequences.

I have always eaten well and exercised, but it became even more import-ant to take good care of myself during my divorce. I was so stressed and couldn't seem to keep anything in my system for a while. I found that totally giving up sugar during that time was very helpful for both my body and my mind. I no-ticed that I felt much better when I ate simple, whole foods like lean proteins and vegetables. My stomach didn't hurt as much and I was able to think more clearly. I needed to care of myself by fueling my body with the foods that would help in my healing.

Sleep is another key aspect for your health. Getting 7-8 hours of sleep each night is recommended for good physical wellbeing. Getting less than that, or more than that, is associated with increased health problems. Plan for eight hours each night. I have always been a light sleeper and insomnia was a major issue for me during my divorce. It was months before I learned things to help me calm my body so that I was better prepared for sleep at night. I had to eat to keep my blood sugars balanced. I needed to have an evening routine that kept me away from electronics an hour before bed. Taking baths with lavender oil helped to relax me as well. There are many things you can do to help your body calm down to prepare for sleep. If you're having trouble, you can try some of the following:

- Take a warm bath.
- Turn off all electronics thirty minutes before bedtime.
- Have a cup of chamomile tea.
- Limit caffeine, even in the morning for some highly sensitive people.
- Read something lighthearted before going to sleep.
- Use blackout shades in your room.

There are many nutritional strategies that have helped people such as supplementing with melatonin, gaba, theanine, and magnesium. Good sleep greatly improves cognitive function and your ability to retain information. Consider working with a nutritionist to see if your diet may be making your situation worse. You may also want to go to a sleep clinic if insomnia is altering your quality of life. Talk with your doctor first to rule out any possible medical conditions.

Getting some kind of physical activity most days of the week will help to keep your weight at a healthy level and increase your energy. It is recommended that you engage in thirty minutes of exercise most days of the week. You don't have to go to the gym. Taking a brisk walk will increase your energy and mood levels, while burning some calories and helping you shed weight. Even ten minutes of strength training can make a difference. If thirty minutes is hard to fit in at one time, split the thirty minutes up and go for ten minute walks a few times a day.

## COMMUNITY WELLBEING

*"THE PERSON WHO TRIES TO LIVE ALONE WILL NOT SUCCEED AS A HUMAN BEING. HIS HEART WITHERS IF IT DOES NOT ANSWER ANOTHER HEART. HIS MIND SHRINKS AWAY IF HE HEARS ONLY THE ECHOES OF HIS OWN THOUGHTS AND FINDS NO OTHER INSPIRATION"*
*-PEARL S. BUCK*

Do you have connections in your community? Do you know your neighbors? Research shows that those who are involved in their community show higher levels of wellbeing (Rath & Harter, 2010). Consider the principles of Weight Watchers or Alcoholics Anonymous. I believe they are successful because they are designed to support people with the same struggle. There's a sense of wanting to do well for yourself, as well as being an encouragement for the others in the group. These kinds of groups can be found in most communities.

What causes are you passionate about? There's probably a local group you could join in for some volunteering in your community. You can make a difference while making new friends that have similar interests. It can also give you a sense of belonging as you work side-by-side with others that share your concern.

Consider where your interests and passions lie. That would be a good place to research options in your local community. Some ideas you could consider include:

- Donating blood at the local blood bank.
- Work with a friend or your family at a soup kitchen.
- Help with a clothing or food drive at a battered women's shelter.
- Offer to help with childcare at a shelter while the parent looks for work.
- Help your local library with their book sales.
- Donate household things to your local thrift shop.
- Help with a community garden.
- Help with yard clean-up for seniors.
- Deliver meals to in-bound seniors with Meals on Wheels.
- Spend time visiting at a nursing home. Some people rarely get visitors.
- Volunteer at a local church.

## HUMAN POTENTIAL

*"DON'T LET LIFE DISCOURAGE YOU; EVERYONE WHO GOT WHERE HE IS HAD TO BEGIN WHERE HE WAS."*
*-RICHARD L. EVANS*

Are you starting to believe that you have more potential than you originally thought possible? If you had asked me if I would be doing what I'm doing now ten years ago, I would have said, "No way." I had to make changes in my life due to my circumstances, but many good things came out of it. You don't have to wait for something bad to happen to you. You can take responsibility for what you would like more of in your life. I personally believe that God is ultimately in control, but he also expects us to use the potential he placed in each of us, and for us to live fully engaged lives that make a difference in our world.

Being fully engaged in life is about being in the flow. Do you ever find yourself so involved in something that you lose track of time? In Flourish: A Visionary New Understanding of Happiness and Wellbeing, Martin E.P. Seligman speaks of five elements for wellbeing which include positive emotion, engagement, meaning, positive relationships, and accomplishment. Positive emotion is when we just feel that life is awesome. Engagement is something that is measured subjectively and involves how absorbed you can become in a project, just for the pure pleasure in it. Meaning is that place where we become a part of something bigger than the self. This is when we feel we are on Earth for a purpose and find fulfillment when we're doing what we were designed to do. Accomplishment is also a part of wellbeing, but it is not as much tied to financial rewards as it is to accomplishing something that matters to us just for the mastery and sake of accomplishment. His fifth element is about having positive relationships. This is where we are engaged with others and offer some sort of kindness to them just for the pleasure and benefit of the other person.

At this time in my life, living purposely matters more. Relationships matter more to me. I love spending time with my children and having them at my table brings back so many wonderful memories. They have become friends now and I'm totally enjoying watching them find success in their young lives. I find myself fully engaged while putting my thoughts on paper. Life is good and my life is being lived on purpose.

Have you ever noticed what happens to people when they go through a crisis? I don't mean during it necessarily, but rather how it changes them over time. You will typically either see someone grow and become a stronger person in time or you will watch them become angry and bitter. In The Me I Want to Be, Ortberg writes, "Rising to a challenge reveals abilities hidden within you (and beyond you) that would otherwise have remained dormant." There is a definite connection between suffering and growth. We will find out how strong we are and what we really are capable of handling when we are forced into an adverse situation. When my marriage first fell apart, I questioned if I would get through it. All I could see at the time was suffering and a trail of devastation. I tried my best to face one day at a time and, over time, good things started to happen inside of me. The inner strength and growth that came were blessings from a bad situation.

For me, adversity was a great teacher. Over the course of a few years, I grew and discovered an inner strength for survival that I didn't know existed in me. "Adversity can deepen relationships…Adversity can change your priorities about what really matters…Adversity points us to the hope beyond ourselves," (Ortberg, 2010). I have seen evidence in each of these statements in my own life. I have had so many great friendships along the way with people that are not afraid to talk beyond the surface. I have found that when I share my vulnerability that it makes it easier for others to share theirs. This has deepened many relationships for me and taken them beyond the superficial level.

I have also noticed that I don't let little things bother me the way they did before. I tend to let people off the hook much easier when they do something offensive. In reality, we all do and say stupid things that we wish we could take back. That's just a part of life. Letting go of offenses and focusing on the bigger picture makes life happier.

I also learned that hard times bring me closer to God. When everything is going well, it can be easy to neglect that spiritual part of yourself, but when life gets hard, we tend to draw on others and our higher power for strength. For me, I find that strength comes when I spend time in quiet reflection, reading inspirational books and in prayer.

### REACHING YOUR POTENTIAL

*"SUCCESSFUL PEOPLE ARE SIMPLY THOSE WITH SUCCESSFUL HABITS."*
*-BRIAN TRACY*

What do you really want in your life? Who are you when you are your best self? How well your life is working five years from now will be based on the choices you make each day along the way. Success will happen when you know what you want and go after it in a strategic, consistent, meaningful and purposeful manner.

A compelling vision statement that identifies what you want, rather than what you don't want, can be a fun project when you want to attract positive change into your life. Most people tend to focus on what they don't like in their life. It's much more empowering to think about the possibilities for your life. A vision statement should be written in the present tense. For example, "I am lean and strong, and thirty pounds lighter. I have reduced my cholesterol and blood pressure levels and enjoy greater energy to do the things that interest me. I enjoy healthier foods and am physically active most days of the week." Keeping this vision in front of you as you work through your weekly behavioral goals will help to remind you of the benefits you will receive.

Another fun project I've used with coaching clients is to create a vision board. You can use a poster board and put pictures from magazines of things you want to do in your life on it. For example, I did one many years ago. I had pictures of my family on it. I had pictures of healthy food and active people. I had pictures of vacation destinations I wanted to go to, and I had pictures of inspirational things. I had this board in my home office and it was a visual reminder of the things I wanted to be the norm in my life. We tend to attract the things that we place before us.

The important part of setting a goal is the person who you grow to be on the journey to accomplishing that goal. There is intrinsic value in what you will learn about yourself along the way. Life is a journey and we are seeking continued progress, not perfection. It's about building new habits. Aristotle once said, "We are what we repeatedly do. Excellence therefore, is not an act, but a habit." If we want different things in our lives, we have to be willing to start doing different things. For instance, if you know your diet needs improvement, just start with one meal and focus on cleaning that up. After you've figured that out and can develop some consistency, add another meal, or focus on your snacks. Small, consistent changes add up over time to new healthy habits.

Setting SMART goals can make the difference between wanting something and achieving it. The principles of SMART goals are:

- Specific
- Measurable
- Action based
- Realistic
- Time sensitive

You start by being specific about the actions and behaviors you will do to accomplish your vision of wellbeing. There needs to be a specific timeline as to when you will achieve the goal. Then, the goal must be measurable—you either did it or you didn't. Setting behavior or action based goals are easier to measure. For example, "I will walk on Monday, Wednesday and Friday mornings for thirty minutes. If it is raining outside, I will use my treadmill." Then, you know the plan to complete the behavior and you have a backup if you can't get outside. The goal is also realistic. I've seen people come into the health club and join and say they will be there six days a week. That is an unrealistic goal for someone to start with that hasn't worked out in the past five years. It's better to start with 2-3 times a week and exceed the goal rather than be set up for failure.

What is it that you would like to be different in your life? Really think about what you would like to be doing consistently in the next three months. Then think about what is realistic six months from now. Some goals will take a few years to accomplish, like going back to school. You are the only one that can change your present situation. Open yourself up to possibilities that you may not have considered in the past. You don't have to have all of the details in place to dream. You'd be surprised what can happen when you start thinking about possibilities instead of limiting yourself to what is true today. Try not to focus on all the reasons it can't work and instead think of all the benefits of achieving your goal.

**Personal Application – Step 5**

1. What would you like to see happen in each of the following areas to bring you greater wellbeing?

• Career wellbeing

• Social wellbeing

• Financial wellbeing

• Physical wellbeing

• Community wellbeing

2. What might your vision statement look like?

# PART 3
# THE PRESENT

# My Life Today

## CHAPTER SEVEN

*"AWESOME PEOPLE HAVE FEAR, DOUBTS, AND WORRIES—THEY JUST DON'T LET THESE FEELINGS STOP THEM! BE AWESOME, KEEP THRIVING, GROWING, INSPIRING AND SHARING."*

*-RICARDO HOUSHAM*

I feel very blessed in life. I remarried four years ago to a man that is loving, supportive and always up for an adventure. We laugh and have fun together. We recently started playing golf together. We have an active social life. I have three grown children, a son-in-law, a daughter-in-law, and three step-children that are all doing well in life. My daughter and son-in-law just made me a grandma to a sweet little baby boy named Jaxon. I cherish all the people I've met along the way.

But my life still has challenges. My mother is in an Alzheimer's unit. It breaks my heart to visit her there every week knowing she is still with it enough to know that something isn't quite right, but not well enough to be on her own for her own safety. I don't see my children as much as I would like. I live just far enough away from them to make it inconvenient to stop by for a short visit, and my oldest lives in another state. However, I am grateful to have all of them in my life, and I recognize how blessed I am.

I recently quit a job that I loved as a corporate Wellness Manager to allow for more time and flexibility in my life. Herman and I like to travel and we will be spending as much of the winter in Naples, Florida in a home we recently built together.

I have accomplished the long-term goal of writing a book and I'm working on my master's degree. Those were goals kept inside of me for a very long time. I'm currently in the process of getting a business up and running as a health coach so that I can still follow my passion of empowering others in their lives, regardless of where I happen to be.

Thriving is a lot about your mental attitude. It's about creating a balanced life where you are more resilient and you can proudly take ownership of your choices. It's about acknowledging where you are today and discovering where you'd like to be in the future.

For me, it means that I'm emotionally and spiritually at peace. I make time for spiritual growth, family and friends. I do my best to be honest with myself as well as those I'm in relationships with.

I don't have as much money in the bank as I'd like, but I have a financial plan. I want to be able to take care of myself as well as leave something for my children.

I am back in school for my master's degree believing that we should always be learning, whether in a classroom or on your own. I have a goal of teaching at the undergraduate college level in the area of wellness. I loved mentoring recent college graduates at my last job and I believe that teaching is a great way to encourage others and help them with their future.

I also plan to continue coaching and speaking. I can't imagine not being involved with helping to improve the quality of life for others.

I am a huge believer in spending time daily reading quality books that enrich your life and add depth to your character.

I exercise most days of the week and fuel my body with healthy food. It really comes down to being intentional with your life.

As a health coach, I teach balance in wellbeing and believe in the 80/20 rule. 80% of the time I do the things that I know are best for balanced wellbeing, and 20% of the time I relax and enjoy something outside of my norm.

I have a few key principles I try to live by:

- Keep your faith and family a top priority. For me, not much else really matters at the end of the day.
- Do your best to be loving and kind to others. You don't know what they're

struggling with. Let go of judgment and try to think the best about others.
- Forgive daily. Refusing to forgive destroys relationships and can poison your soul. Everyone messes up at some point and needs a break.
- Have written goals in the key areas of your life so that you can look back next year and see all the progress you've made. It can be very powerful.
- Realize that it's NEVER too late to go after your dreams.
- Do your best to live with integrity and ethics. Change what you can and let go of the things that you can't change.
- Consider what you want to be remembered for and live that way now.

I hope to be remembered as being loving and kind, tender hearted and forgiving.

# *ABOUT THE AUTHOR*

Joan is a health coach that has worked both as a corporate Wellness Manager for Fortune 500 companies and in her own business. She specializes in the area of nutrition and exercise and empowers those in mid-life to shed the weight that has kept them from fully participating in the life they want to live. As manager of a national weight loss center and in her own business, Joan has helped hundreds of people over the years lose weight and gain their health back.

Joan holds a B.S. in psychology and a B.S. in holistic nutrition. She is currently a candidate for her M.S in exercise science and health promotion with a concentration in wellness coaching and plans to complete that in 2016. Wellcoaches Corporation certified her as a Health and Wellness Coach in 2007. To stay on top of her nutrition knowledge, she is enrolled in the Institute of Integrative Nutrition's health coach training and will graduate in March of 2016. Joan holds several credentials with the National Academy of Sports Medicine, along with a host of other certifications in stress management, fitness and yoga.

# WORKING WITH JOAN

As a health coach, I will help you create greater wellbeing. Together, we will develop your wellness vision, set appropriate goals, and help you do it in a way that feels empowering and achievable. The goal is self-efficacy for lasting change. Here is what past clients have said about working with me:

*"I truly loved your presentation at the "Loving Your Heart" seminar this morning. Your insight into what is really important in life—loving ourselves and incorporating healthy habits in order to build a strong mind, body and soul was inspiring. It's the little things—staying positive, being motivated and surrounding oneself with good people that play an important role in being healthy. Thank you for offering tips to help us stay healthy and recognizing some of the things we need to shed and the beauty in ourselves that we need to share."*

## -GO RED TEAM/MEDTRONIC

*"Joan is excellent as a nutritional consultant because she understands that each person has different challenges and responds to different motivation. I learned that change is a process."*

## -J. DELAGO

*"Joan truly loves what she does and it shows in her dedication to helping people reach their goals. She is very knowledgeable about fitness as well as nutrition. She continues to keep me motivated and focused on reaching my goals."*

## -S. JACOBSEN

*"Joan's sessions were so encouraging and inspirational. Why did I wait so long? She helped me discover my weak areas and tackle them."*

## -M. LUND

*"The changes in my health, as seen in the results from 2013 to 2014 health screenings, proves it! Joan—thank you! I am positive this would not have happened without your knowledge and support!"*

### -B. STANEK, ORBITAL/ATK

*"Thanks for being here and being an ear to my weight loss questions. Somehow you have inspired me to lose weight in a way that seems simple with positive, lasting results. You listen and guide without preaching. Your guidance on diet has been particularly helpful."*

### -D. SAKRY, ORBITAL/ATK

*"Working with Joan brought about the results I needed and wanted. She took into consideration the realities of my personal and professional workload and devised a practical approach to lose weight and feel better about my body. She guided me positively to make better nutrition choices and pushed me when I needed to be pushed in the gym. Joan has a talent for getting results in a practical manner."*

### -M. BARNETT-LIVGARD

# RESOURCES

To discover your signature strengths, go to www.authentichappiness.org and take the Values in Action Signature Strengths (VIA) test. It's a free assessment that will help you understand what your character strengths are. It's an interesting tool to help you better understand yourself as you look at who you are at your inner level. Some people never take the time to think about these things. Understanding what traits make up who you are may ultimately help you find direction.

**I recently took mine and found these to be my top five strengths:**

1. **Honesty, authenticity, and genuineness**
2. **Spirituality, sense of purpose, faith**
3. **Hope, optimism, and future-mindedness**
4. **Industry, diligence, and perseverance**
5. **Curiosity and interest in the world**

What I choose to do in life should line up with my signature strengths. I hope this tool is helpful for discovering things about yourself.

# REFERENCES

Knabb, J. "Centering Prayer as an Alternative to Mindfulness-Based Cognitive Therapy for Depression." *Journal of Religious Health* (2012): 51,908-924.

"Listening to the Warning Signs of Stress." *apa.org*. APA. Web. 19 September 2015.

Moore, M. & Tschannen-Moran, B. *Coaching Psychology Manual*. Philadelphia, PA: Wolters Kluwer/Lippincott Williams & Wilkins, 2010.

Ortberg, J. *The Me I Want To Be*. Grand Rapids, MI: Zondervan, 2010.

Powers, S. K. & Howley, E. T. *Exercise Physiology: Theory and Application to Fitness and Performance. (8th Ed.)*. New York, NY: McGraw-Hill, 2012.

Rath, T. & Harter, J. *Wellbeing: The Five Essential Elements*. New York, NY: Gallup Press, 2010.

Made in the USA
San Bernardino, CA
24 November 2015